Game Boy Galactic

by

Alan Durant

Illustrated by Sue Mason

You do not need to read this page – just get on with the book!

First published in 2009 in Great Britain by
Barrington Stoke Ltd
18 Walker St, Edinburgh, EH3 7LP

www.barringtonstoke.co.uk

Copyright © 2009 Alan Durant
Illustrations © Sue Mason

ISBN: 978-1-84299-661-4

Printed in Great Britain by Bell & Bain Ltd

AUTHOR ID

Name: Alan "The Guvnor" Durant

Likes: Football, my family, my very old car, reading, burping.

Dislikes: January, stewed apple, oven cleaning, fighting, EastEnders.

3 words that best describe me:
Tall, dark, handsome liar (oops, that's four).

A secret not many people know:
I am heir to the throne of Bogzania
(and I once crashed my bike into a bubble car).

ILLUSTRATOR ID

Name: Sue Mason

Likes: Cycling on my pink bike, trees, having clean teeth, forward rolls, sunshine, a good lip balm, my brilliant friends.

Dislikes: Removing tangles, the smell of fried bacon, sleet, tingling lips from raspberry blowing, broken umbrellas.

3 words that best describe me:
Susannah Jane Mason.

A secret not many people know:
I have this dream a lot in which I can fly to tree height after eating pink custard powder from a tin.

For my nephew and niece,
Christopher and Caroline.

Contents

Level 1

Muzzy ran. His feet slid on the loose stones of the broken road, but he ran. He had to. The soldiers were on their way to his village. In moments they would be there with their guns. They would take any man or boy who had not run away and they would shoot them. Muzzy's mum had told him so. So now Muzzy was running after his dad through the dark. They were running for their lives.

Kaboom!

Something exploded on the road behind Muzzy. It threw him forward.

"Agh!" he cried.

His feet slipped and he fell. This was it. He couldn't run any more. He started to cry.

"Muzzy!" His dad was standing over him, shouting. "Muzzy, get up!"

A hand grabbed his arm and yanked him up.

"Muzzy, run! You have to run!" His dad pushed him on. Muzzy ran.

Muzzy and his dad ran and ran. First they ran from their village into the hills. Then they ran over the hills to the border at the edge of their country. They ran from the enemy soldiers and they ran from the border police. They ran on and on ...

At last they had some luck. They found a lorry with its back doors open. They jumped in. They hid in a small space behind some big wooden boxes. The doors shut. The lorry drove away.

Muzzy and his dad were in the lorry for a long time. It was very dark. It was hard to breathe. Muzzy wanted to be back home with his mum and his sisters. He was scared. Sometimes he wanted to scream but he had to be as silent as a butterfly – like the ones in the field above his village where he and his sisters played.

Finally the lorry stopped. The doors opened. Light came in. Air came in. Muzzy could breathe at last. He gulped down the air.

Muzzy and his dad were in another country. They had escaped. Now, they were refugees, looking for a safe place to live.

And, for Muzzy, that was just the start of the problem.

Level 2

Muzzy went to school in his new country but he found it hard. He didn't understand what people were saying. It wasn't easy to make friends. Some children laughed at him. Some children pushed him in the playground. They told him to go back to where he came from. It made him sad because that is what he wanted more than anything. But he couldn't go back. His dad said that they had to stay here until the war in their own country was over and it was safe to return.

Muzzy was a fast learner. Soon he started to speak and read in his new language. Some nights he even dreamed in it. He had many nightmares about the soldiers chasing him. But his worst dreams were about being in the back of that lorry, silent, not able to breathe ...

There was a boy at school called J P. He was kind to Muzzy. He knew that Muzzy didn't have any toys or games. One day he gave Muzzy a present. It was a Gameboy Advance.

"I don't use it any more," he said. "You can have it."

Muzzy had never seen a Gameboy before. He didn't know what it was or what it did. He was amazed when J P turned it on and showed him how to play a game.

"Thanks," Muzzy said and he did something that he hardly ever did – he smiled.

Muzzy and his dad lived in a room in a house with other refugees. Muzzy's dad had a job at the rubbish tip. It was dirty and smelly but Muzzy's dad didn't mind. He knew how hard it was to find work.

That evening, Muzzy showed his dad the Gameboy that J P had given him. Muzzy's dad was very surprised, but pleased.

"I'm glad you're making friends," he said.

The next evening Muzzy's dad had a surprise for Muzzy.

"Look what I found on the tip," he said.

It was a Gameboy game! Well, it looked like one. It didn't have a title on it, just one line of print. Some of the words were very hard to read. Muzzy read them out slowly, "Warning! This experience may seriously damage your health." What did it mean?

The next morning Muzzy put the new game in his Gameboy when he was walking to school. The Gameboy came to life with a ping!

"Hi, Muzzy!" A girl called out to him as he walked by. It was Mia. She was playing with her little brother Zak.

"Hi, Mia," Muzzy replied and he waved. Seeing Mia and Zak playing made Muzzy think of his sisters. He missed playing with them.

All of a sudden Muzzy had a weird feeling that someone was watching him. He looked across the street. There was a man in a telephone box staring at him. The man was wearing thick glasses. His eyes were huge and seemed to gleam as if someone was

shining a torch into them. He had a cone of white hair on top of his head. He smiled at Muzzy, showing a row of silver-capped teeth. The man gave Muzzy the creeps. He walked faster.

He looked down at his Gameboy. The game was loading up. A new message flashed up on the screen.

"Warning!" Muzzy read. "Once you start there is no going back." *How true that was*, Muzzy thought. He couldn't go back to his country.

"Muzz-ee! Muzz-ee!" Voices called out behind Muzzy. But these weren't the voices of friends calling. They were the nasty, mocking voices of the bullies from school. He turned around, saw them moving quickly towards him. He turned away and ran.

Level 3

Muzzy ran past houses and shops. His feet were thumping the pavement. The game was still on in his hand. He looked down at the Gameboy screen. It showed a strange red landscape. Red mist was rising from the ground. Muzzy looked up again. He frowned. "Wh-what?" he uttered.

Ahead of him puffs of red mist were rising. The grey pavement had gone. The ground was red now and more like earth than concrete. Muzzy looked down at his hands and saw the Gameboy game was no longer there. He turned. The bullies were nowhere to be seen. He stopped running and peered about him. It was like he had been sucked into the game and was playing it from the inside! But how could that be? And where was he now?

Something glinted at Muzzy through the red mist. He moved towards it and came to a pile of rocks. The glinting thing was a shiny stone, like a crystal. Muzzy bent down and picked it up. The crystal glowed on his hand. It made Muzzy feel warm and strong. J P had told him in some games there were tokens to collect. They were good for you. They made the game easier to play. Muzzy put the stone in his pocket and moved towards the next glinting crystal. Soon he had picked up six stones. *What now?* he thought.

There was a loud hum in the air. A round silver space-ship was flying in the pink sky.

The space-ship had a kind of metal arm. It moved from side to side. Now it was pointing towards Muzzy. At the end of the arm was a huge, green jelly eye. It was staring right at Muzzy and it made him shiver. It was scary. But what happened next was much more scary. There was a whooshing noise and a beam of light shot out from under the space-ship and hit the ground just in front of him. There was a flash of fire and smoke rose. Muzzy jumped back. If that beam had hit him, he would have been burnt up! Someone was trying to kill him!

Muzzy threw himself behind a tall pile of rocks. Whoosh! The space-ship fired again. Crash! The rocks were blown away. Muzzy wasn't hurt but now he had nowhere to hide. The space-ship had moved on but now it was coming back. The giant eye was looking for Muzzy again. What could he do? His eyes fixed on the pillars of mist. Perhaps he could hide inside one of those. He worried for a moment that the mist might be a poison gas, but it was his only chance. He sprinted to the nearest pillar of mist, waited for a second, then stepped inside. The red mist swirled round him.

He heard the hum of the space-ship above him, waited for the beam blast ... but none came. The space-ship moved away. It would come back, though, Muzzy was sure of that. He couldn't stay here for ever. He looked out at the landscape around him. There was a large hill in the distance. If this was some sort of a game then perhaps that was the end of the level. There was nothing else in sight, apart from the pillars of mist and piles of rocks. He made up his mind to go towards the hill. He waited until he heard the hum of the space-ship move away again, then he dashed to the next pillar of mist. It closed round him like a cloak. The space-ship couldn't see him.

He made his way towards the hill, moving from misty pillar to misty pillar. It was slow going, because he had to wait until the space-ship had passed over before he dared go out into the open. J P had told him that there was a time limit to these games. If you went over the limit, you lost tokens or a life. Muzzy wondered if he'd lose some of his shiny stones, because getting to the hill was taking him a long time.

At last, he was inside the last pillar of mist and the hill was right in front of him. But what now? Should he climb the hill? But the space-ship's giant eye would soon see him and then he'd be an easy target for its killer beam.

Then he saw it – the opening to a cave, half-hidden behind rocks at the bottom of the hill. He didn't have to climb the hill, he had to get inside it!

The cave was about 50 metres away, much further than the distance between the misty pillars. He would have to move at just the right moment and run very fast ...

The space-ship hummed in the sky, coming closer. Muzzy started to run the instant it past over-head. He was very good at running. He ran like he was being chased by the soldiers in his homeland or by the bullies in his new country, he ran for his life.

But five metres from the cave opening disaster struck – Muzzy tripped on a stone and fell head-first. "Ow!" His ankle hurt.

He heard the hum of the space-ship getting closer, louder. Looking up, he saw the giant jelly eye glaring down at him. He stared back, not able to move. Then he heard his dad's voice shouting in his head, "Muzzy, get up, run! You have to run!"

Muzzy pulled himself to his feet, trying to ignore the pain in his ankle and ran. His heart was thumping. Would he make it? He heard the whoosh of the space-ship's burning beam, he threw himself forward into the cave, felt fire scorching his feet ... Then everything went black.

Level 4

Muzzy blinked. He had expected to be in darkness, but he was in daylight. There was a new and surprising world *inside* the hill. But then everything was surprising now. He was inside a hill inside a Gameboy game and he'd completed the first level (how many more levels would there be?).

Perhaps most surprising were the colours. In the beautiful garden before him, the plants and leaves weren't green but purple. They were strange shapes too. There were plants like elephants' trunks, giant bells, jumping jacks, cabbages on sticks and huge sharp spears. He knew that this was a game, though, so he would have to play in some way. He felt in his pocket. Three of the six stones had gone. He'd been right then – there had been a time penalty in the last level. He'd have to be quicker.

Muzzy started walking, making his way through the tall plants. He hadn't gone far when he saw that he was in a maze. So, that was the game!

He needed to put down a marker of some kind, so that he wouldn't keep going back along the same path. In school they'd read a story about a Greek hero called Theseus. He had had to get in and out of a maze to kill a monster who was half man and half bull. It was called the Minotaur. The hero had escaped the maze by putting down rope behind him as he went. What could Muzzy use? He looked around and saw what he needed. One of the plants had vines growing off it. He pulled hard and a long line of vine came away. He coiled it around his arm. Then he started walking again, dropping one end of the vine behind him.

Muzzy walked fast. He went up and down the paths of the maze. He seemed to be going in towards the centre. He was starting to think that maybe he'd been lucky and chosen the right way first time. But then he came to a dead end. He broke off the vine then walked back the way he'd come until he found another path he hadn't yet been down. He let the vine trail behind him again. He came to another dead end ... and another.

He stopped in front of a wall of bright flowers. They were like water lilies, the kind that grew in the warm water of his village pond. They were yellow in the middle with bright purple petals. His sisters called them gas jets, because that's what they looked like – lighted jets of flame on a gas stove. He reached out a hand to touch one and "Ah!" He cried out and pulled back his hand. The flowers really were like flames and they burned his hand! He blew on his hand and shook it. This place wasn't like his home. He couldn't trust anything. Even if it looked harmless, it might be a danger. He was inside a deadly game and he had to be careful. He put his hand in his pocket and wasn't surprised to find that another of the crystals had gone.

Muzzy walked down another path – and another, careful not to touch the sides of the maze where the bright flowers grew. He was getting tired. Surely he must come to the centre of the maze soon – and when he did? What then? What would he find there? What if he were walking into a trap? But he had no choice. His only way out was to keep looking for the centre.

He had no more vine left to put down as a marker. He looked around for something else to use. There was another rope-like plant coming out of the maze wall in front of him. That would do. He reached up and grabbed at it.

All of a sudden, arms sprang out from the plant and grabbed him. They wrapped around him like the tentacles of an octopus and started to crush him. He could hardly breathe. He felt faint. He struggled but the tentacles were too strong. They were squeezing the life out of him. He didn't even have enough breath in him to cry out. He moved his head around, his mind searching for an escape. He was running out of time.

Just as he was giving up hope, he saw the gas-jet flowers. An idea came into his head. With one last effort he turned in the octopus plant's grip and pushed back so that one of its arms rubbed against the gas-jet flowers.

In seconds the arm burst into flame! Then another one did the same. There was a terrible screeching and the arms let go of their grip on Muzzy. He rolled free. Then he got to his feet and ran.

The next path he went down took him to the centre of the maze. He ran through it. The maze vanished.

Level 5

Muzzy took a deep breath. He'd got through another level – but only just. What dangers awaited him now? In front of him the ground was bumpy, cracked and orange like honey-comb. To the right, bright yellow steamy springs shot up. To the left, pools of mud as brown as chocolate bubbled. Beyond all of this, a huge, silver citadel shone. Muzzy was sure that that was where he had to get to. That must be the heart of this strange game.

He started walking again, taking a path between the steaming yellow springs and the bubbling mud. He felt a bit like the girl Dorothy in that film they'd watched at school one wet lunch time. *The Wizard of Oz*, it was called. She had to follow the yellow brick road – he had to follow the orange cracked path. It was a nice thought somehow. He'd liked the film. It had a happy ending. Thinking about it made him feel more relaxed ... too relaxed. He didn't see what was slithering out of the cracks in the ground, until it was almost too late.

They were disgusting. They were red, squashy and slimy like slugs but hairy too like caterpillars. They had long feelers at the front and hissed like cockroaches as they slithered. Muzzy heard the noise before he saw them. He looked down and saw one of them slithering over the trainer on his left foot. He kicked hard, but it held on, moving towards his leg. He kicked at the giant insect with his right foot and it flicked off into the air with an angry squeal.

Muzzy felt a sharp prick at the back of his left leg, just above the ankle. He looked down and saw another of the slimy insects on his leg, sucking. He cried out and whacked the thing away with his hand. It left a trickle of blood on his skin where it had pricked him.

More and more of the insects were crawling up. They were all around him now, oozing out of the ground, their long feelers waggling. He couldn't get to the citadel this way. He'd have to choose one of the other paths – the yellow springs or the bubbling mud pools? He was sure from the way steam was rising from the springs that they must be burning hot. The mud pools then.

He went quickly towards them and was about to step in when he stopped. What if there were other things in among the

bubbling mud? The pools were so dark he couldn't see what might be hiding in them. Back in his own country one of his friends had been killed by stepping on a mine that he hadn't seen. The mine had exploded. No, he'd much rather see any danger that was waiting for him.

Muzzy turned and leapt over a swarm of the giant sucking insects and ran across to the yellow springs. He stopped for a moment to watch them. He saw how the springs came out of the ground getting taller and taller, making an arch, until they dropped down again. There was a second's break and then they shot up once more.

He could feel the heat of the springs from where he was standing. He was sure the yellow liquid would burn him badly if it went on his skin. But how was he going to get through the springs without getting burnt? He thought about the controls on the

Gameboy. If he were playing, what would he do? Of course, he'd *roll*! As soon as the yellow springs started to rise, making their arches, he'd roll and hope that he'd be fast enough to get through before they dropped back down.

He needed to act fast because the slithery, sucking insects were getting closer. And not only that – from out of the bubbling mud pool a monster was rising!

The springs started to get taller. Muzzy bent down, ready to roll. The monster roared. Muzzy threw himself forward and rolled for his life. Drops from the yellow springs fell about him, spitting and sizzling like acid. Steam scorched his ears, but he kept rolling, over and over. He was almost at the end of the springs. They were dropping now, and fast. There was hardly any gap for him to get through. He closed his eyes, threw himself forward again, keeping as low as he could ...

He landed with a bump on the dry ground and rolled once more. He looked up. He was through! He'd made it! The mud monster was beating its chest and roaring. Its teeth were huge. Thank goodness he hadn't chosen to go through the mud pools!

He got to his feet and ran towards the citadel.

Another level had been completed.

Level 6

Above the citadel gates a red warning
sign flashed: *Enter at your peril!* Muzzy
stared at the words. He didn't know the word
peril, but he thought it must mean danger.
Someone was warning him that it would be
dangerous to go into the citadel. Well, he
didn't need to be told that! The last stone had
gone from his pocket. He must have lost it
when the insect sucked his blood. So now he
had nothing to help him. He really was all on
his own.

He walked towards the gates and they slid open. He stepped inside.

It was amazing. There were cameras and screens everywhere. He looked up at a screen and saw himself on it! He waved. On the screen he waved too. For a moment he thought of the old TV in his house. The picture was always fuzzy, but every night he and Dad and the other refugees sat and watched it. They waited for news about their home country. But the news was always bad.

In front of Muzzy long, silver escalators flowed up and down. Muzzy loved escalators. The first time he'd seen one was when he'd first come to his new country. He'd run up and down, up and down until he was dizzy.

At the top of the escalators was a square platform. That must be where he had to go.

Muzzy stepped on to the escalator going up. He watched himself on the screens as he climbed. He grinned and pulled silly faces. He stuck out his tongue and ... what was that? A figure appeared on the screen behind him. It had a warty green face with one glowing red eye. It was holding a gun ... and the gun was aimed at him!

Muzzy threw himself down. A burst of flame passed over his head. He looked up and on the screen he saw the alien moving away. It must have been on another escalator – one going down. He'd been too busy staring into the screens to see it. And now another alien with a gun was coming down towards him.

Muzzy got ready. The alien came closer. When they were level with each other, the alien raised his gun and fired. But Muzzy had already ducked down and the gun fire passed over his head with no harm done.

Muzzy shook himself into action. He started running up the escalator. Each time

he drew level with an alien, he ducked down. He had to get his timing just right, but he did it. He got to the top of the escalator and jumped on to the platform.

Muzzy looked about him. There were tube-like tunnels all around the citadel. In the middle was a crystal dome. Muzzy was sure that's where he needed to get to.

There was a kind of car in front of Muzzy. It was small and see-through. On the side it said *Pod 327*. More aliens were coming towards Muzzy. He didn't stop for a second. He climbed inside the pod car. The roof closed over him. The controls lit up. On the control panel a word flashed in red: *Drive*. Muzzy put his foot on the pedal. The car shot forward.

The pod car sped down a tunnel. Muzzy steered to the left and then to the right. He was going towards the crystal dome. He hoped that there he might find out how to get out of this game. How long had he been on this alien planet?

"Hey!" Muzzy cried as something swooped down at him. It was a sort of metal bird, like a bat. It had a beak like a spear-head. Muzzy swerved just in time. "Clank!" the bat's metal beak hit the side of the pod, denting it.

Muzzy turned another corner. More of the metal bats flew towards him. Muzzy looked down at the controls. There was a red button on the wheel. He pushed it in.

Tatata-tatata-tatata-tat! A line of bullets fired from the front of the car. As the bats came near, he pushed the button again. *Tatata-tatata-tatata-tat!* The bats exploded one after another.

Muzzy steered the car to the right into another tunnel. More bats swooped at him. Once more, he waited till they were close and then pushed the red button. *Tatata-tatata-tatata-tat! Tatata-tatata-tatata-tat!* Bat after bat exploded.

The bats came thick and fast. There were too many now for Muzzy to shoot them all. He tried turning into other tunnels, left and right, left and right, not going straight towards the crystal dome but taking a round-about way. It seemed to work. After a while, the bats stopped swooping. Muzzy was glad. The bats with their spear beaks had been scary.

But Muzzy still wasn't safe. All of a sudden another pod car came racing along the tunnel towards him. Muzzy pushed the button and fired, but a shield went up at the front of the other pod and the bullets bounced off. The pod sped closer and fired its gun at Muzzy. He had no time to get out of the way of the bullets. He looked down quickly at the controls. There was a green

button. He pushed it. A shield popped up. The bullets from the other pod hit the shield with a pop-pop-pop. But they didn't get through. He wasn't hurt.

Muzzy wasn't out of danger yet. The other pod was still speeding on and it was aiming right at him. It wasn't going to stop. It was going to crash right into Muzzy's pod!

Muzzy held the wheel steady. He had to be strong and brave. He must not flinch or turn too early. He had to keep his nerve.

The two pods raced towards each other. On and on they rushed. It seemed that they must crash ...

But right at the very last moment, Muzzy turned the wheel hard to the left and his pod swerved away. The other pod carried on down the tunnel and round the corner. Muzzy took a deep breath. That had been too close – much too close.

He drove on with great care to the end of the tunnel, turned right ... and there it was – the crystal dome!

Level 7

Light was everywhere. It gleamed, glinted, sparkled and flashed. Muzzy was amazed. It really was like being inside a giant crystal.

Muzzy looked about. There was no one in the room, just a huge blank screen that hung from the roof. No aliens then. That was good. He was feeling tired now. He didn't think he had the energy to fight off any more aliens – or metal bats or slithering insects or swamp monsters. He just wanted to be out of here, for the game to end, so that he could go home. But then he thought about the bullies waiting for him ...

Why was everyone always chasing him, trying to harm him? What had he done wrong? He hadn't hurt anyone. All he wanted was to live in peace – to be back home. But where was home?

All of a sudden, as if in answer to his question, a message flashed up on the screen: *You have played well. Pass the final test and you may leave this galaxy and go home. The Controller.*

Muzzy blinked at the screen. "How?" he said aloud.

A new message appeared: *You must face your fear.*

Muzzy shook his head. Face his fear! How many more fears did he have to face?

Another message: *No. Your true fear. The thing you fear the most. Face your fear and you will be free. Run from it and you will die.*

The words melted away and pictures formed on the screen of alien guards, all heavily armed, marching towards the crystal dome. Muzzy couldn't run any longer. He was trapped. He'd have to face his fear. But after all he'd been through, how bad could that be? He could face anything, couldn't he?

"Tell me what I must do," he said.

The answer came at once: *Enter the box and take hold of the galactic crystal.*

Muzzy frowned. What box? He searched the dome with his eyes.

Then he saw it – a small opening, leading into a narrow tunnel and, at the end of it, a box hardly big enough for him to fit into. A dark, airless space, like the one on the lorry he and his dad had hidden in on their escape.

Muzzy stared at the box in horror. Already he could feel himself gasping for air, his heart racing, panic making his hands and fore-head wet with sweat.

He couldn't do it.

A loud noise made him look back at the screen. The marching guards were almost at the entrance to the crystal dome, their guns in front, ready to fire. In a few moments they would be inside and Muzzy would have no chance. There were hundreds of aliens, all with one aim – to kill him.

Muzzy looked at the box again. He started to shake. This was the nightmare he feared more than any other – having to go into that tiny place. And once he went in, there was no way he could get out.

The doors to the crystal dome began to slide open.

Another wave of panic hit Muzzy.

He couldn't do it.

But he had to.

"Go on, Muzzy!" In his head, his dad's voice urged him on.

The doors were almost open.

He looked up at the screen. A thought suddenly struck him. *It's a game, Muzzy, just a game. You can't be beaten by a game!*

He took a deep breath. As the first alien entered the dome, Muzzy squeezed through the opening and into the tunnel. It was so narrow that he could hardly move. But he forced himself on ... and on, until he came to

the small box. A last wriggle and he was inside.

On the wall in front of him was the galactic crystal, giving out a faint glow in the dark, stuffy space. Muzzy tried to breathe, but there was no air. He reached out a trembling hand and grabbed the crystal.

For a moment he thought nothing was going to happen. The Controller had tricked him.

Then the dark exploded into light – and his lungs filled with air. His feet touched concrete.

He'd done it. He'd escaped!

Level 8

Muzzy looked at the screen. *Well done! You have won! Want to play again?*

Muzzy frowned. He didn't feel like he'd won. He felt like he'd escaped. No way did he want to play again!

"Muzz-ee! Muzz-ee!" He'd forgotten about the bullies. They'd caught up with him now, their mocking voices right behind him. He moved to start running. Then stopped. He'd escaped from soldiers that wanted to kill him and from the scariest game in the world.

What were a few bullies compared to that? It was time to stop running. It was time to face his fear.

Muzzy turned and the bullies almost ran into him. They looked at Muzzy in silence for a moment or two. They hadn't expected him to stop.

"What you got there, Muzzy?" said the leader of the bullies at last, nodding at Muzzy's hand with a mocking look.

"It's a Gameboy," Muzzy replied. "J P gave it to me."

"J P?" the bully repeated.

"Yes, he's my friend," said Muzzy.

"You ain't got no friends," sneered the bully. Muzzy thought the bully might make a grab for the Gameboy, but he didn't. People

liked J P. He had a lot of friends. The bully didn't want to pick a fight with him.

"You should go back home. We don't want you here," said the bully.

Muzzy looked the bully in the eye. "This is my home now," he said. "I'm not an alien. I live here like you."

The bullies looked at each other. They didn't seem to know what to do. The leader took a step forward.

"What's that game you're playing?" he demanded. "Did your friend give you that too?"

Muzzy shook his head. "No. My dad found it on the rubbish tip. But it's not really a game, it's an experience. A really scary one."

The bullies laughed. "You'd better give it to me then," said the leader. "We don't want little Muzzy getting scared by a bit of rubbish." He put out his hand for Muzzy to give him the game.

"You don't want it," Muzzy said. "It's bad. It could kill you."

The bullies thought this was the funniest thing Muzzy had said.

"I mean it," Muzzy insisted.

The leader of the bullies held out his hand. "Give it to me," he said.

Muzzy gave a shrug. "If you really want," he said. He took the game out of his Gameboy and handed it to the bully.

"Cheers, Muzz-ee," crowed the bully and he marched away, followed by the others.

"Hey, Muzzy!" J P was waving at him. Muzzy waved back and grinned. He had a sudden feeling of happiness. He felt like he belonged.

Across the street, the man with the cone of white hair watched the two boys walk away together and smiled. Behind his thick glasses, his odd eyes glinted like crystal.

Barrington Stoke would like to thank all its readers for commenting on the manuscript before publication and in particular:

Kamahl Ahmet
Bradley Arnott
Ella Louise Atkinson
Luke Belcher
George Bell
Amy Berrisford
Bethany Brown
Sam Clegg
Calluinn Cooke
James Cutts
Shirley Davids
Alexander Dawes
Cameron Dewar
Thomas Dunne
Ben Farrar
Lewis Forfoot
Callum Franklin
Alfie Hanvey
Joseph Hird
Chloe Hynes
Hara Gonzalez
Harry Little
Flora Manning

Chloe McKell
Lewis Metcalfe
Fay Mitchell
Issac Moore
Charlotte Murgatroyd
Jake Newell
India Gabrielle Porter
Ruben Ritterband
Jobe Saint
Rosa Sargent
Ryan Silk
D. Short
Chris Sloan
Charlotte Tett
Amelia Thompson
Ruby Thorpe
Toby
Joel Tulloch
Molly Upton
Keziah Watts
Sam Whitford
Jessie Woodhouse
Dan Woodus

Become a Consultant!

Would you like to give us feedback on our titles before they are published? Contact us at the email address below – we'd love to hear from you!

info@barringtonstoke.co.uk
www.barringtonstoke.co.uk